PUZZLES FOR THE HIGH IQ

Lloyd King

Edited by Philip J. Carter

SCHOLASTIC INC.

New York Toronto London Auckland Sydney
Mexico City New Delhi Hong Kong

To my family and friends

ISBN 0-439-08244-7

12 11 10 9 8 7 6 5 4 3 2   9/9 0 1 2 3 4/0

Printed in the U.S.A.   40

First Scholastic printing, September 1999

CONTENTS

ACKNOWLEDGMENTS

I'd like to thank Philip Carter for kindly coming to my aid and rescuing both me and the manuscript. Without his generous help the project would surely have foundered. I'd also like to thank my mum, Mardi, my sister, Hannah, the rest of my family and all my friends for their support and encouragement. I'd like to thank Scot Morris for his helpful suggestions; Cassell PLC for permission to republish several puzzles; and *The Sunday Times*, specifically, for permission to republish the brainteasers "Code" (Number 11) and "Number Crunching" (Number 29), both of which first appeared in *The Sunday Times* magazine, London.

PREFACE

The puzzles in this book have been designed to be both amusing and challenging. At first glance you may find that some look a bit daunting, but, rest assured, you do not need any specialist knowledge to solve them. If you approach them in the right way, using lateral thinking and by being open to new, creative solutions, you will find that you come up with many, if not all, of the correct answers. It may be a relief to you to know that most have the kind of answers that just "jump out" at you, so no laborious calculations are necessary. Often a typical reaction on finding out an answer to such a problem is to smile and say, "Of course!", while wondering why on earth you didn't think of such a "simple" answer in the first place. I hope you have a lot of fun solving the puzzles, and perhaps you will be inspired to try to create a few of your own.

Lloyd King

PUZZLES

1   SEQUENCE

What letter, apart from E, can be added to the following to complete this sequence?

S E Q U E N C _   (Solution 109)

2   SERIES

Which is the missing figure in this series?

?

Choose from:

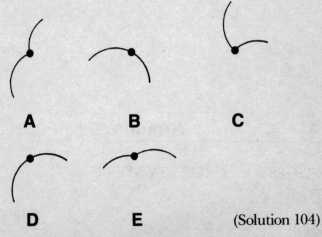

A   **B**   **C**

D   **E**   (Solution 104)

Arrange the fish below in such a way that you produce the same number of fish facing in each of just two opposite directions. Every fish must face in either of these two directions.

(Solution 99)

FISHES is to SCALES as WATER is to ?

(Solution 94)

What should go in the top box?

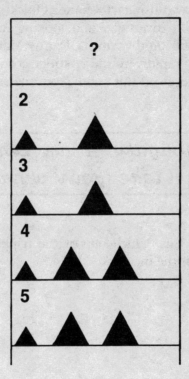

(Solution 89)

6   **SEQUENCE**

The question mark in the sequence below represents a letter. Which letter?

123, 451, 46733, 8197, 80?3   (Solution 84)

Sherlock Holmes was relaxing in his study when, suddenly, a snowball struck one of the windows overlooking the street below, causing it to shatter. Quickly, he went over to the window to investigate and, looking out, just caught sight of the Willoughby triplets, Danny, Mark and Oliver, disappearing rapidly round a street corner. The next morning he received this anonymous message:

> ? Willoughby. I am certain he broke your window.

According to this, which one of the triplets should he question about the incident?

(Solution 79)

What comes next in this sequence?

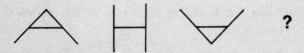 ?

Choose from:

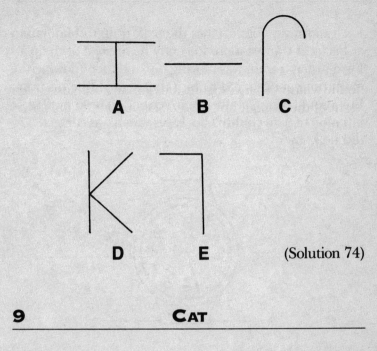

A   B   C

D   E   (Solution 74)

9   CAT

Rearrange five toothpicks to leave another cat going in the opposite direction.

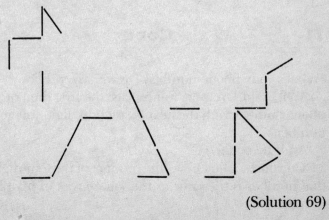

(Solution 69)

Each morning Tom catches the 6:42 train to Manhattan at his local train station. Recently he arrived at the platform just as a train was moving out and, not knowing the exact time, it occurred to him that it might be his train. But after glancing at his watch (see below) he knew that, if it was on time, it couldn't be. If his watch was correct, how did he know?

(Solution 108)

11   CODE

"What's your phone number, Drew?" asked Eliot.

"Well," said Drew, "if you replace the first digit of your phone number with the next lowest odd digit, you get my number."

"And the code?"

"Curiously," said Drew, "the product of the four digits in that number is the same as the square root of my phone number."

"But that's insufficient information," pointed out Eliot.

"Yes," said Drew, "But if, in addition to that information, I were to tell you the sum of those four digits, then you'd have enough."

What is Drew's code? (In Britain the "code" is four digits.)

(Solution 103)

12   ANALOGY

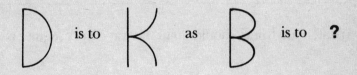

Choose from:

A   B   C   D   E

(Solution 98)

What is the next word in this sequence?

REDDEN
SEAM
BLEW
HATRED
DENSE
AMBLE
?

(Solution 93)

14 SPOTS BEFORE YOUR EYES

What, if anything, should go in the two empty segments?

(Solution 88)

15   ODD ONE OUT

Which is the odd one out?

> A   TOR
> B   SHOP
> C   RATE
> D   RECTOR
> E   SIGN
> F   ANTIC   (Solution 83)

16   SUBSTITUTION

If TA times I equals CAB, and TE times TILE equals CLOTH, what does TO times IN equal—BAT, HINT, POISON, TABLE or TOOL?

(Solution 78)

17   SOMETHING IN COMMON

What fairly unusual feature do these words have in common?

> Cling
> Drive
> Fort
> Motion
> State   (Solution 73)

What letter comes next?

D U I I U IV ?

(Solution 68)

The black windows in the hotel below indicate the positions of elevators (known as lifts in Britain). Can you figure out which other window should be black?

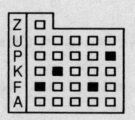

(Solution 64)

Below are five cocktail sticks arranged to create a glass containing a cocktail stick. Add another cocktail stick to the arrangement so that it sounds as though it is empty.

(Solution 107)

21   **SERIES**

The following series is incomplete. Can you find the next figure?

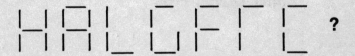

Choose from:

A   B   C   D   E

(Solution 102)

Rearrange three lines to leave a three-dimensional picture of another horse.

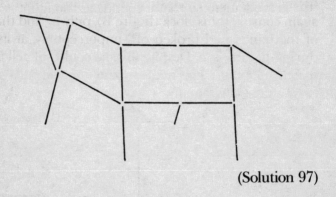

(Solution 97)

23 **SHORT LIST**

Which word continues this short list?

**Embark, Cotton, Ochre, Calm,
Small, Duvet, Frost,   ?**

Choose from:

Dell, Flute, Globule, Orange, Plume.

(Solution 92)

At thirty-four minutes and fifty-eight seconds past three Joe noted the time on his clock (figure A) and set off on his daily jog. When he returned less than an hour later he again consulted his clock (figure B), only to find that one of the hands had broken off, imperceptibly, at its base during his absence. Despite this, he could still tell immediately for exactly how many minutes *and* seconds he had been away. Can you?

A

B

(Solution 87)

Every member of the Lutulu tribe on the island of Olapu is either a Gugu, who always tells the truth, or a Mumu, who always lies.

An anthropologist revisiting the island cannot recall whether there are nine or ten Mumus, so when she meets the tribe's chief she asks him how many of his people are Mumus, forgetting that he too is either one type or the other. Fortunately, when he tells her how many of them are, she remembers this fact and, although she cannot determine which group he belongs to, she can figure out how many Mumus there are.

How many are there?

(Solution 82)

26   SYMBOLS

Can you find the missing symbol?

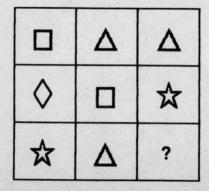

Choose from:

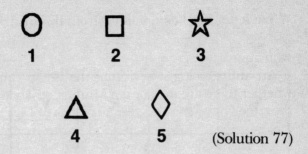

1   2   3

4   5   (Solution 77)

27   ODD ONE OUT

Which is the odd one out?

(Solution 72)

What letter has been omitted from this grid?

T	C	K	Y	C
G	E	N	C	A
L	Y	C	N	S
M	A	L	M	C
S	E	C	U	?

(Solution 67)

29   NUMBER CRUNCHING

Exactly one digit in each of the following ten numbers is in the same position as it is in Sam's five-digit (British) phone number:

01265
12171
23257
34548
45970
56236
67324
78084
89872
99414

What is his number?   (Solution 61)

30   SPOT CHECK

Below are two complete views of a die and another that is incomplete. How many spots could be missing from the third view: 2, 3, 4, 5 or 6?

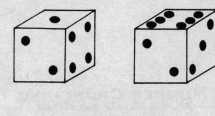

(Solution 106)

During her math class Katie had to arrange some toothpicks to create two sums, in Roman numerals, which she then had to solve. Originally she got sum A right and sum B wrong. Unfortunately a toothpick has since been removed from sum A so that it now appears to be wrong and, as a strange consequence, sum B now appears to be right. Can you reconstruct sum A?

$$V - IV = IV$$

A

$$V + IV = IX$$

B

(Solution 101)

This is a cryptogram where every letter of the alphabet has been substituted for another. The spaces between the words have been closed up and some words continue on the next line. To help you, half of the letters of the alphabet have been placed in a table. When the rest are placed correctly in the bottom row you will find that each of the letters in each column can be replaced by the other in the cryptogram to leave two lines from a well-known poem followed by the author's name.

ETJZHQUEVWDJKMJKXWGKHVJR

GKIJKMGVWKEOVFDHTGKWETHQ

UZTFVG-HGQQDGITJHHTUQFVMQ

UKJDGWZFKHTGKWETH'ZBQYHF

KWJKZTFVG!GMEJVJQQJKBFG.

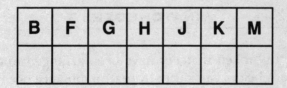

B	F	G	H	J	K	M

Q	U	V	W	X	Z

(Solution 96)

Can you find the end number?

   **?**

Choose from:

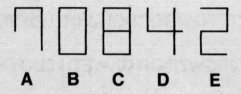

A   B   C   D   E

(Solution 91)

34   **MATCHBOXES**

Some unbroken matches have been arranged to create figure A below. Curiously, by rearranging just one match it is possible to create figure B. How is this possible? (NB. The figures are not actual size.)

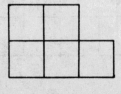

A

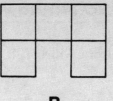

B (Solution 86)

35 SERIES

The following progression of figures is based on a well-known, elementary series. Can you find the next figure?

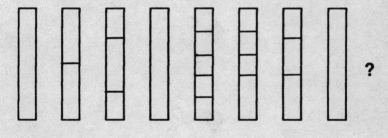

?

Choose from:

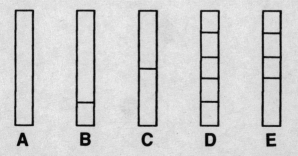

A   **B**   **C**   **D**   **E**

(Solution 81)

Can you discover from which fish the black square is missing?

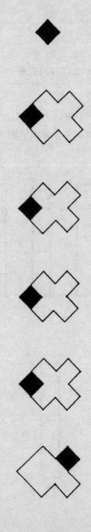

(Solution 76)

Which is the odd one out?

BULL
COW
CRAB
GOAT
LION
RAM
SCORPION

(Solution 71)

38   **CLOCK SEQUENCE**

Can you add two more lines, the same length as those below, to complete this clock sequence?

(Solution 66)

39   THE NIGHTMARE BEFORE
CHRISTMAS

It was getting very late on Christmas Eve and Santa Claus still had toys to deliver to the kids in four more villages. The toys, all identical, were distributed equally in four identical sacks, each of which contained toys for the kids in just one of the villages. However, just two of the villages had the same number of kids as there were toys in any one sack. The other two, Alphaville and Betaville, had either too many or too few. Therefore, to put things right Santa took two of the sacks to one side and either removed two toys from the one for Alphaville and put one of those in the one for Betaville, or removed two toys from the one for Betaville and put both of those in the one for Alphaville. Unfortunately, while he was looking for some labels for the sacks, one of the elves unwittingly put both sacks back with the other two, so he could not then easily identify them.

After thinking for a while, he decided to find them by carrying out various weighings using a two-pan balance scale with each pan containing two of the sacks, and to make his task less confusing, he numbered the sacks 1 to 4. However, after just one weighing, which revealed simply that sacks 1 and 2 were heavier than sacks 3 and 4, the balance scale broke.

If the sacks for Alphaville and Betaville are, in no particular order, either 1 and 2 or 2 and 4, which sack should Santa deliver to which of these two villages?

(Solution 63)

A prince asks the king of a neighboring land for his daughter's hand in marriage. The mischievous king tells him that he will only consent to the marriage if the prince can arrange ten coins to form the phrase "I consent". The prince takes out ten coins from his pocket and begins to arrange them on the table in front of him. But no matter how he positions them he cannot form the phrase.

Can you help him?

(Solution 105)

KIW is to RKRHE as WANIB is to ?

Choose from:

ATOQ

FRNH

HOLP

NZED

UCAN

(Solution 100)

What number completes this series?

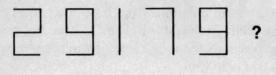 **?**

(Solution 95)

43   DIGITAL CLOCK

At 16 minutes past two one afternoon Carla, who does not know the time, consults her digital clock. It shows 2:17. How does she know it is incorrect?

(Solution 90)

44   MERRY-GO-ROUND

Dizzy was enjoying a wild ride on a merry-go-round with some friends when the following occurred to her:

"Although there are 12 in all in the merry-go-round, not 11, it is possible to arrange those in the merry-go-round so that there are both 10 in front of me and 10 behind me."

Using the diagram of a merry-go-round below, can you explain what Dizzy means?

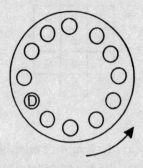

(Solution 85)

45 THROUGH THE LOOKING-GLASS

After reading Lewis Carroll's *Through the Looking-Glass*, Anna set about the math homework she'd been putting off all weekend. She multiplied 50 by 1415.58 on her pocket calculator and found to her surprise that the word *error* could be seen on the display. If she performed the calculation correctly and the calculator did not malfunction, what is the explanation?

(Solution 80)

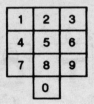

The digit buttons on Mr. Knight's telephone are arranged as above. If his nine-digit telephone number contains nine different digits and the first six digits are 0, 6, 1, 8, 3 and 4, respectively, what are the last three digits?

(Solution 75)

47   SERIES

What single letter can be arranged in the following series to complete it?

?B?DEFG??JKLMNOPQRS?UVWXYZ

(Solution 70)

Which option completes the following?

Choose from:

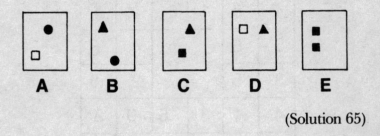

(Solution 65)

What is the next letter in this sequence?

(Solution 62)

There are 28 tiles in a set of dominoes with each half of each tile carrying a number of spots from 0 to 6, so that every possible pair of numbers appears exactly once. The arrangement below contains 16 dominoes from the same

2	5	2	6	3	5
4	5	1	6	4	4
5	6			4	6
3	5			2	6
4	1	3	6	0	3
5	5	3	6	4	6

set. The numbers indicate the number of spots originally on each half. You will see that one half of one of the dominoes has no spots. Can you work out how many spots are on its other half, i.e., is it 0,2; 0,3; 0,4 or 0,6?

(Solution 6)

Can you complete this necklace?

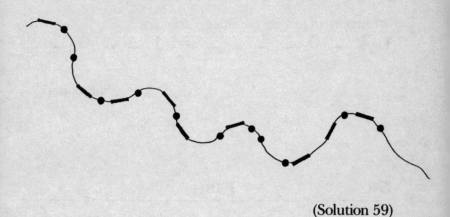

(Solution 59)

52   **SOMETHING IN COMMON**

What do all of the following words have in common?

ALP
BET
THE
LAMB
UPS

(Solution 53)

Can you complete this weighty equation so that both sides balance?

1 4 _ 0 _ _ _ _ = 1 _ _ 0 _ _

(Solution 47)

Which figure is next in this series?

     ?

Choose from:

  A   **B**   **C**   **D**   **E**

(Solution 42)

is to as is to ?

Choose from:

1

2

3

4

5

(Solution 36)

Can you solve this alphametic in which each digit has been substituted for a letter?

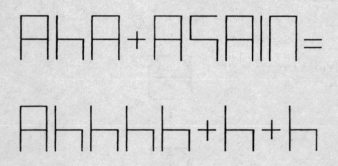

(Solution 30)

What is the eighth figure in this series?

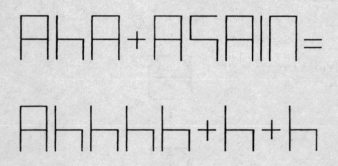

(Solution 24)

What is missing from the following?

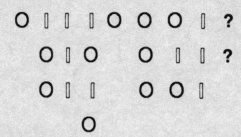

(Solution 18)

Which is the odd one out?

PAW
TOW
MILL
OMEN
ROMAN
WILES

(Solution 12)

Can you find the missing figure?

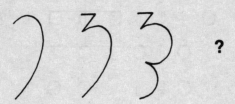

?

(Solution 5)

61   PARALLELEPIPED

A cube has a different letter on each of its sides. Below are two views of the cube. Can you figure out what letter should replace the question mark on the flattened cube?

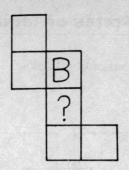

(Solution 58)

62　　　HIDDEN LOGIC

Can you find the hidden logic and then choose the next figure?

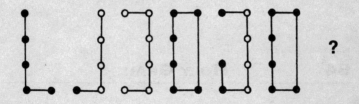

Choose from:

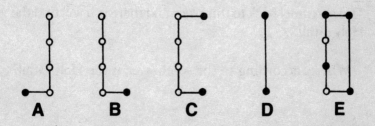

(Solution 52)

What letter has been omitted below?

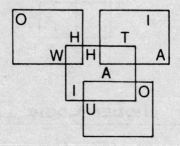

(Solution 46)

Sir Galahad was in the Holy Land searching for the Holy Grail when he came across a soothsayer who said to him:

"Take a camel back to this place and there you will find the Holy Grail."

Where, according to the soothsayer, is the Holy Grail?

(Solution 41)

"Dad, what's this week's winning lottery number?" asked Chloe.

"Coincidentally," he said, "exactly one digit in each of the five columns in the previous six winning numbers on this piece of paper is in the same position as one of the digits in this week's winning number."

"Thanks, Dad." said Chloe, looking at the numbers over his shoulder. "But I can't determine the number from that information."

Chloe showed the numbers to her mom.

```
0 9 9 0 6
0 1 6 9 1
8 9 6 8 9
0 9 6 0 9
1 9 6 8 9
8 6 8 8 9
```

"Your dad's right." she said. "Exactly one digit in each of the five columns *is* in the same position as one of the digits in this week's winning number, which, incidentally, is . . ."

"Thanks, Mom," interrupted Chloe. "But I now know what it is."

What is this week's winning number?

(Solution 35)

Can you decode the following pop song?

DA DODODODO DO DA

DODO DADA DO

DODODO

DA DODODODO DO

DADODADA DODA

DODADO DO DODA

DADODADO

DODODODO

DODA DADO

DADADO

DODO DADO

(Solution 29)

Early one evening a shiftworker sets the alarm on his bedside clock to wake him when the hour hand points to the hour division line marked "ll". Why, when his shift at a nearby factory starts at 2:30 A.M.?

(Solution 23)

68   **CAPITAL SURPLUS**

Rearrange the seven shapes below to leave a capital E that is vertically symmetric and has three prongs of equal length. None of the shapes may overlap.

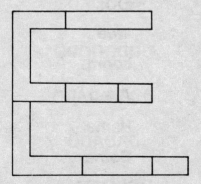

(Solution 17)

The positions of which two words in the following list should be swapped?

Ass

Llama

Ceres

Eel

Nereus

Rune

Ocean

Near

Deer

Eros

Woe

Loom

Anna

Name

Dome

(Solution 11)

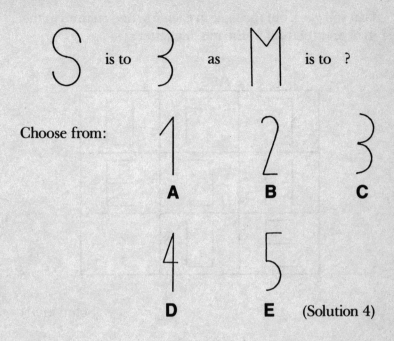

S is to ℨ as M is to ?

Choose from:

A   B   C

D   E   (Solution 4)

71 **SEQUENCE**

What letter, apart from W, can be placed next to the V to leave a straightforward sequence?

V?XYZ

(Solution 57)

Can you work out the logic in each row and column in the grid and then fill in the missing letter?

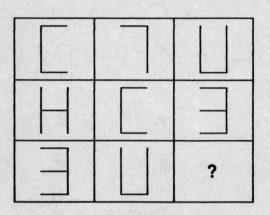

(Solution 51)

What is the next number in this sequence?

| 5, | 5, 6, 9, ?

(Solution 45)

Can you rearrange 5 straight lines to leave a Japanese make of car?

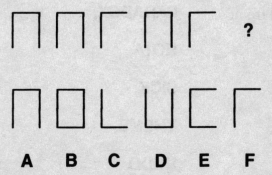

(Solution 40)

Which letter comes next in this series?

∏ ∏ Γ ∏ Γ   ?

∏ ∐ L U Γ Γ

A   B   C   D   E   F

(Solution 34)

Which word should replace the question mark below?

| 9 □ | 9 9   = **LOUNGE**

| □ | | 9   = **PETROLEUM**

| | 9 9   = **?**

Choose from: **PARADOX,**

ROTA,

SICK,

THEME,

UNDO.

(Solution 28)

What four-letter word has been omitted below?

LOVE

EMOTIVE

ENDLESS

SUEZ

****

MEANDER

(Solution 22)

What letters should replace the asterisks?

	W	E	R	*		*	I	*	*			
	A	*	D		G	*	*	*	*			
			*	*	*	N						

(Solution 16)

Can you find the misfit?

> **MALI**
>
> **INDIA**
>
> **NEPAL**
>
> **SPAIN**
>
> **FIJI**
>
> **INDONESIA**
>
> **TURKEY**   (Solution 10)

Can you find an eight-letter word to replace "*", which when placed below the eight pairs of letters forms eight three-letter words reading down?

P   B   C   T   B   S   H   A

E   U   A   O   A   K   A   R

—   —   —   —*—   —   —   —

(Solution 3)

Which figure has been omitted below?

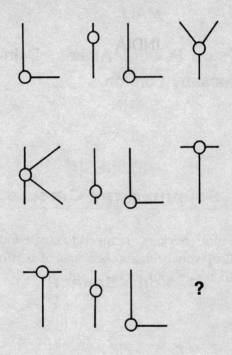

Choose from:

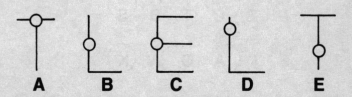

(Solution 56)

In which single six-letter country can the following capitals be found?

**Oslo, Peking, Athens, Delhi,
Nassau, London.**

(Solution 50)

83   SQUARING THE CIRCLES

Below are nine checkers arranged to create four identical squares. Can you find another way of arranging nine checkers to create four identical squares?

(Solution 44)

Which of the options—A, B, C, D or E—completes the
following?

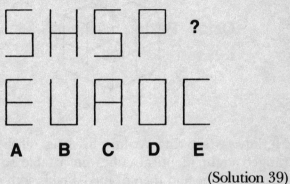

(Solution 39)

85   **DOMINO EFFECT**

Rearrange three dominoes to leave a capital E without
serifs.

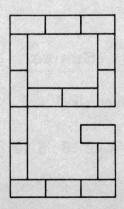

(Solution 33)

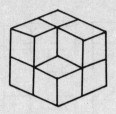

Merlin was showing Arthur his latest illusion. He arranged eight identical cubes on a table so that they formed a cube and then draped a tablecloth over them. Next he waved his magic wand and one of the cubes rose up under the tablecloth and moved to a position just in front of the arrangement of cubes. Finally, he removed the tablecloth. Where Arthur had expected to see the cube, there was now apparently nothing to be seen. If in fact the cube is still visible, where is it?

(Solution 27)

87   Series

What is the seventh number?

0 1 4 2 8 5 ? 1 4

(Solution 21)

Which is the missing figure?

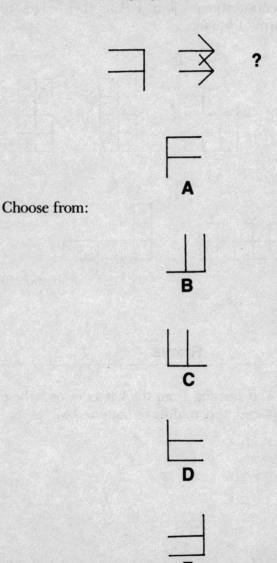

Choose from:

A

B

C

D

E

(Solution 15)

Rearrange 5 of the 6 polyominoes, each of which is a set of 7 or 8 identical squares joined along their edges, to produce a form of square.

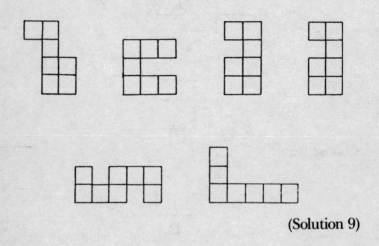

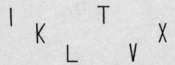

(Solution 9)

90 ROWS

If the letter Y is missing from the letters below, where should it be placed: top, middle or bottom row?

I   K   T   V   X
L

(Solution 2)

Remove one match to leave 23.

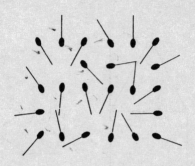

(Solution 55)

What is the missing word?

O ■ ▲ ☆ = **W A I L**

☆ ◆ ▽ ♣ = **L U R E**

♠ ■ ☆ ♥ = **? ? ? ?**

(Solution 49)

Can you rearrange six toothpicks to leave the "bear" much further away from the cabin?

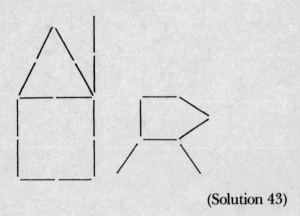

(Solution 43)

94   HEXOMINOES

Which one of these seven hexominoes cannot be arranged with five of the others to form a six by six square?

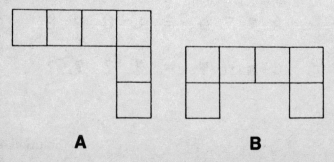

A   B

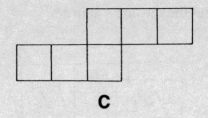

C

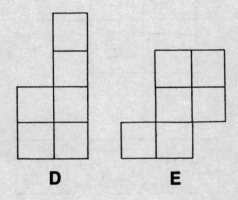

D   **E**

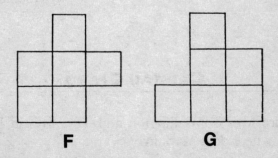

F   **G**

(Solution 38)

Can you find the missing square?

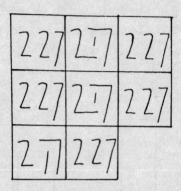

Choose from:

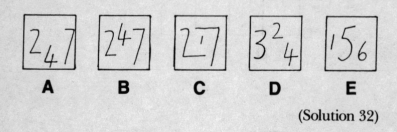

A   **B**   **C**   **D**   **E**

(Solution 32)

If Erica lives in Washington and Tina lives in Buenos Aires, where does Mark live?

(Solution 26)

Can you find the missing number?

$$5+1+6 = 7$$
$$5+1+642 = 70$$
$$4+6 = ?$$

(Solution 20)

Which is the next figure in this series?

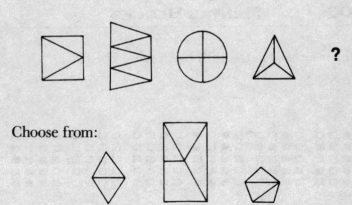

Choose from:

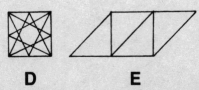

A   B   C

D   E

(Solution 14)

Early one evening in nineteen ninety-four a would-be time traveler pressed a button on his time machine. Seconds later its digital display indicated that it was eighteen fifty-eight, next that it was eighteen fifty-nine and then that it was nineteen hundred! Can you say what the display showed next?

(Solution 8)

Which squares in the fifth block should be black?

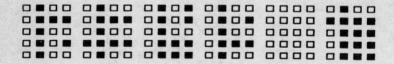

(Solution 1)

101   THE MISSING NUMBER

Can you find the missing number?

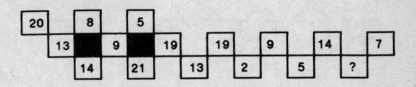

(Solution 60)

102   ODD ONE OUT

Which is the odd one out?

BOLMA
CML
CONVMAL
LMD
OBLMOUS
TRMAL

(Solution 54)

Which is the next figure in this sequence?

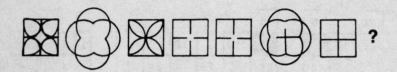

Choose from:

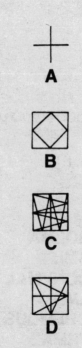

A

B

C

D

E

(Solution 48)

What word or phrase is represented by each of the following?

XYZABC
1

GLIBNESS
2

ooooo🔌
3

P L O▟
4

TSETAOCRUMP
5

CO IFER
6

(Solution 37)

Which is the next figure in this sequence?

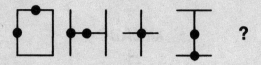 ?

Choose from:

(Solution 31)

Recently Watson received this puzzling message from Sherlock Holmes:

> *Meet me outside the village railway station tonight at ?*

At precisely what time does this message tell Watson to meet Holmes?

(Solution 25)

107   SOMETHING IN COMMON

What do all of these words have in common, apart from having four letters?

DATA

MANE

MONA

TEAS

VENT

(Solution 19)

What is missing from this series?

| ⌐ ⌐ | | **?** | ⌐

(Solution 13)

109   **NUMBER SEQUENCE**

Can you add 3 more lines to complete this number sequence?

⌐| | | |⌐| 6 2 |

(Solution 7)

SOLUTIONS

1. Move the blocks together and you will see that the white squares form the series 1, 2, 3, 4, 5, 6.

(Puzzle 100)

2. The middle row.

(Puzzle 90)

3. Asterisk.

(Puzzle 80)

4. A. The left halves of the first and third figures are folded over their right halves to form the second and fourth figures.

(Puzzle 70)

5. The figures are the right halves of card suit symbols.

(Puzzle 60)

6. 0, 6. The total number of spots in a domino set is 168. Therefore, the total number of spots on the 12 dominoes not in the arrangement is 38, a total which can only be achieved by adding up the spots on the following dominoes: 0,0; 0,1; 0,2; 0,3; 0,4; 0,5; 1,1; 1,2; 1,3; 1,4; 2,2 and 2,3. The only remaining domino with no spots on one half is 0,6.

2	5	2	6	3	5
4	5	1	6	4	4
5	6			4	6
3	5			2	6
4	1	3	6	0	3
5	5	3	6	4	6

(Puzzle 50)

7.

(Puzzle 109)

8. 19:01. His "time machine" is actually a 24 hour digital clock.

(Puzzle 99)

9. It is impossible to arrange the polyominoes to form a square shape because the total number of squares they are formed from is incorrect. But, . . .

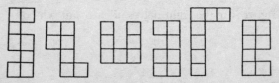

(Puzzle 89)

74

10. Nepal. The initial letters of the other words spell misfit.

(Puzzle 79)

11. Rune and Woe. The tall letters spell . . .

ALICE IN WONDERLAND.

(Puzzle 69)

12. Paw. The others are men's names with one letter inverted:

PAM, TOM, WILL, OWEN, ROWAN, MILES.

(Puzzle 59)

13. ⌐ The figures are the tops of the numbers in the series 1, 2, 3, 4, 5, 6, 7 as shown below:

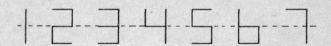

(Puzzle 108)

14. E. A sequence is formed by the letters V, W, X, Y and Z contained within the shapes.

(Puzzle 98)

15. E. At the right end of each horizontal line is a V-shaped element which rotates 45 degrees clockwise to produce each new figure.

(Puzzle 88)

75

16. As you can see, it is part of a keyboard.

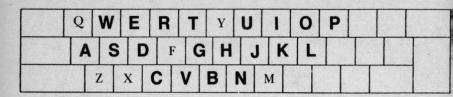

(Puzzle 78)

17. Here is one possible solution:

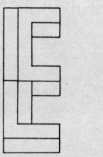

(Puzzle 68)

18. ▯ Rotate the whole thing 90 degrees counterclockwise
▯ to find MORSE CODE in Morse code.

(Puzzle 58)

19. Each word is formed from the first two and last two letters of an American state, i.e., DAKOTA = DATA, etc.

(Puzzle 107)

20. 10. Each number and plus sign represents a letter in the following number, i.e., 4 = T, + = E, 6 = N.

(Puzzle 97)

21. 7. This is one seventh in decimal form without the decimal point.

(Puzzle 87)

22. Zoom. The first letter of each word is the same as the last letter of the preceding word.

(Puzzle 77)

23. His clock has Roman instead of Arabic numerals.

(Puzzle 67)

24. ⊥⊤ Rotate each line 90 degrees about its center to get the series 1, 2, 3, 4, 5, 6, 7, 8.

(Puzzle 57)

25. Nine on the dot. The "question mark" is actually a 9 on a dot.

(Puzzle 106)

26. Copenhagen. Each person's name is the end of the name of the country in whose capital city they live.

(Puzzle 96)

27. If you stare at what seems to be the space left by the cube, a levitating cube appears.

(Puzzle 86)

28. Sick. The spaces between the numbers in each row form a word which is a synonym of the word to its right, e.g.,

(Puzzle 76)

29. Each DO and DA is short for a DOT or a DASH in Morse code.

The song is Bob Dylan's

The Times They Are A-Changin'.

(Puzzle 66)

30. 868 + 85810 = 86666 + 6 + 6. The letters are actually the tops of the numbers in the equation.

(Puzzle 56)

31. A. The horizontal lines in the first figure move to its center to produce the second figure. The vertical lines in this figure then move to its center to produce the third figure. In this figure each of the two horizontal lines moves in the same direction as before to the place occupied by the other in the first figure to produce the fourth figure. Similarly, the fifth figure is produced by moving each of the two vertical lines in the fourth figure in the same direction as before to the place occupied by the other in the first figure.

(Puzzle 105)

32. C. Each number is a shadow letter on its side. Rotate the grid 90 degrees clockwise to find three words reading across: SEE, EGG and GEE.

(Puzzle 95)

33.

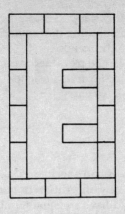

(Puzzle 85)

34. F. The two rows are the tops and bottoms
of the series A, B, C, D, E, F.

(Puzzle 75)

35. 16891. Chloe's mom and dad looked at the numbers opposite
ways up.

(Puzzle 65)

36. 5. Each of the figures has been created by superimposing the
letters of a number. The first number figure is one less than the
second, so the third should be one less than the fourth, i.e.,

the unscrambled analogy is

ONE is to TWO

as

FOUR is to FIVE.

(Puzzle 55)

37.
1. Ecstasy
2. Blessing in disguise
3. Innuendo
4. The plot thickens
5. Storm in a teacup
6. No entry   (Puzzle 104)

38. F. If the hexominoes had alternating black and white squares, F would be the only one with a different number of each. Since a six by six square would have an equal number of such black and white squares this rules out F. The square may be formed by arranging the other six hexominoes as follows:

(Puzzle 94)

39. C. The words SEA, HUB, SAC, POD and ACE can be found by reading down each column of letters.

(Puzzle 84)

40.   TOYOTA

(Puzzle 74)

41. Camelot.

Camel + ot (back to). (Puzzle 64)

42. C. The figures are joined-up Roman numerals, i.e.,

 CXI = 111,

 CX = 110.

The answer is, therefore, or CIX, which equals 109.

(Puzzle 54)

43.

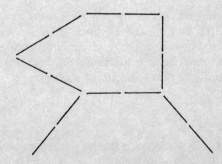

(Puzzle 93)

44.

(Puzzle 83)

45. 51. The 1 moves from one side of the 5 to the other in equal stages.

(Puzzle 73)

46. O. Superimpose the four rectangles to get the names of three American states reading across.

(Puzzle 63)

47.   14POUNDS = 1STONE.   (Puzzle 53)

48. A. The figures in the top row have been formed from the letters B, C, D, E, F, G and H. Each letter has been reflected laterally and a duplicate of the resultant figure rotated 90 degrees counterclockwise. The next figure should therefore be formed in this way from I, the next letter in the sequence.

(Puzzle 103)

49. Halo. The black and white shapes represent vowels and consonants respectively.

(Puzzle 92)

50. Poland. The "capitals" referred to in the question are the initial letters of the listed capital cities.

(Puzzle 82)

51. F. The last figure in each column and row is formed from the parts of the two preceding figures which would not coincide if they were superimposed.

(Puzzle 72)

52. D. If you pay attention to the spots only, and completely disregard all the lines, you will be able to see the word "logic" in alternating black letters and white letters.

(Puzzle 62)

53. They are all the beginnings of Greek letters.   (Puzzle 52)

54. Each option is actually a word in which the I, V and I have been moved together to form M:

> BOLIVIA
> CIVIL
> CONVIVIAL
> LIVID
> OBLIVIOUS
> TRIVIAL

> The odd one out is   BOLIVIA
> because all the others are adjectives.

(Puzzle 102)

55. If you pay attention to the match heads only and completely disregard the rest of them, you will be able to see the number 29. All you have to do then is remove the appropriate match to leave the number 23 as follows:

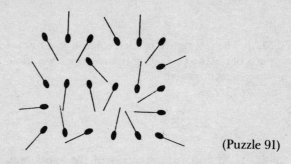

(Puzzle 91)

56. A. Each white disc conceals a part of each letter which if isolated would correspond to a smaller version of that particular letter. These letters form the same word in each row as the larger ones.

(Puzzle 81)

57. V, because when placed next to the V it forms W. (Puzzle 71)

58. O, so that the letters on the flattened cube spell cuboid.

(Puzzle 61)

59. The round and rectangular beads represent the dots and dashes of Morse code.

They spell NECKLACE. (Puzzle 51)

60. 18. Each number represents a letter of the alphabet where A = 1, B = 2, C = 3, etc. The phrase spelled out is THE MISSING NUMBER.

(Puzzle 101)

61. 30274. In all there are ten digits correctly positioned. The first column contains all of the digits, so one of them must be correctly positioned. In the last four columns a total of nine correctly positioned digits can only be achieved if the last three digits of Sam's number are 2, 7, and 4, respectively. Although this means that the first digit must be 3 and that, therefore, none of the digits in the second column is correctly positioned, the second digit can still be determined because only one digit, zero, has been omitted from this column.

(Puzzle 29)

62. V. Each small letter is formed by folding the bottom half of the preceding large letter upwards over its top half.

(Puzzle 49)

63. He should deliver number 2 to Alphaville and number 4 to Betaville. The combined weight of both of these sacks could be either lighter than or equal in weight to the other two sacks. However, because Santa chooses to weigh the four sacks in this manner to detect the two different sacks, those he is attempting to find must be equal in weight to the other two, otherwise he could not find both sacks, just the lightest one. The heaviest sack, 2, is therefore for Alphaville and the lightest one, 4, is for Betaville.

(Puzzle 39)

64. Each window represents a letter of the alphabet, and the letters run from bottom to top and from left to right. The first letter of each row is indicated on the hotel's sign. The black windows coincide with the letters in the word lifts.

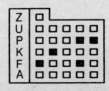

(Puzzle 19)

65. E. When this option is placed in its appropriate position the question mark becomes P and the word stop is completed.

(Puzzle 48)

66.

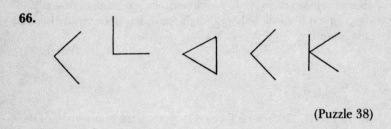

(Puzzle 38)

67. L. The Cs are actually incomplete Os. Each row of the grid contains the name of a city.

(Puzzle 28)

68. I. The row of letters is the bottom half of the word bottom.

(Puzzle 18)

69. The word cat can be formed from shadow letters going from left to right as follows:

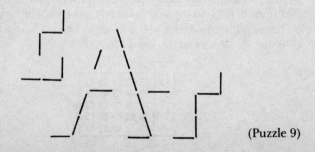

(Puzzle 9)

70. Arrange the letters in the word "aitch" (H) in their appropriate places in the series.

(Puzzle 47)

71. Cow. The others are signs of the zodiac.　　　(Puzzle 37)

72. Y. Each of the others has two lines of equal length, whereas Y has three.

(Puzzle 27)

73. If you pronounce the first letter of each word as an individual syllable you get a new word: ceiling or sealing, derive, effort, emotion, estate.

(Puzzle 17)

74. B. Each of the two long lines in each figure rotates forty-five degrees to produce each new figure. The left one rotates counter-clockwise and the right one clockwise.

(Puzzle 8)

75. 927. His number is generated by moving from one button to another like a chess knight without revisiting any button. This diagram shows how a knight moves in chess:

	X		X	
X				X
	.	K		
X				X
	X		X	

(Puzzle 46)

76.

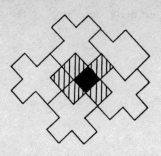

(Puzzle 36)

77. 3. Substitute each symbol in the grid for the appropriate number from the row of symbols so that each row and column totals 10. (Puzzle 26)

78. Poison. Substitute each "times" for X. (Puzzle 16)

79. Mark. Substitute "?" for Question Mark. (Puzzle 7)

80. She found that the answer, 70779, reads error when viewed in a mirror.

(Puzzle 45)

81. A. The figures in the top row are the letters A to H viewed from the right, so the next figure must be I viewed from the right. (Puzzle 35)

82. Nine. Here is a table showing the chief's possible answers, etc.:

	ANSWER	DEDUCED NUMBER OF MUMUS
If a Gugu	9	9
	10	10
If a Mumu	8	10 (9 + chief)
	9	9 (8 + chief)
	10	9 or 10 (8 or 9 + chief)

The anthropologist could therefore only determine how many Mumus there are and not know which group the chief belongs to if he answers nine.

(Puzzle 25)

83. Place letters in the spaces to get 6 words:

> ACTOR
> BISHOP
> CURATE
> DIRECTOR
> ENSIGN
> FRANTIC

> FRANTIC   is the odd one out
> because all the others are occupations.

(Puzzle 15)

84. V. Each of the other letters in the series one, two, three, four, five has been substituted for a digit.

(Puzzle 6)

85.

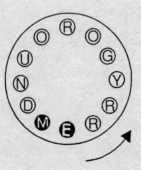

(Puzzle 44)

86. Both figures are an enlarged, head-on view of the ends of five matches.

(Puzzle 34)

87. 35 minutes and 12 seconds. His clock is an alarm clock and it was the alarm hand which broke off.

(Puzzle 24)

88. Nothing. Each circle contains a view of one of the eight corners of a die.

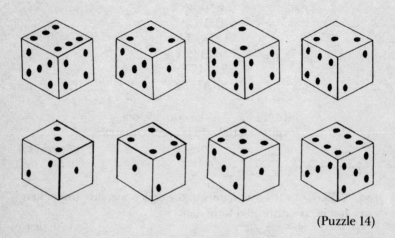

(Puzzle 14)

89. It is the two, three, four, and five of diamonds placed on top of each other so that only their tops are visible. Logically, the ace, which represents one in a pack of cards, should be at the top.

(Puzzle 5)

90. It is a 24-hour clock.

(Puzzle 43)

91. D. Each figure has one more termination than the previous one.

(Puzzle 33)

92. Dell. If you look at the lower case letters and those without ascenders, you will see a list of colors running through the words—maroon, cream, mauve, and rose.

(Puzzle 23)

93. What. The question tells you the answer. The first 17 letters are repeated in the same order.

(Puzzle 13)

94. Air. In the Zodiac the Fishes is a water sign and the Scales is an air sign.

(Puzzle 4)

95. ⵊ, so that when viewed in a mirror the series reads "series."

(Puzzle 42)

96.

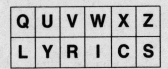

Place the title of the puzzle in the table as shown above to enable you to get the following:

> GHASTLY GRIM AND ANCIENT RAVEN
> WANDERING FROM THE NIGHTLY SHORE—
>
> TELL ME WHAT THY LORDLY NAME IS
> ON THE NIGHT'S PLUTONIAN SHORE!
>
> EDGAR ALLAN POE.

(Puzzle 32)

97.

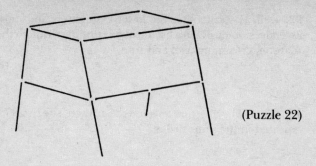

(Puzzle 22)

98. A. The top and bottom halves of the first and third figures move down and up, respectively, to produce the second and fourth figures.

(Puzzle 12)

99.

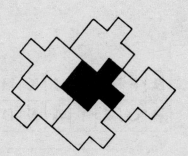

(Puzzle 3)

100. UCAN. The whole sentence is simply a list of birds—Kiwi, stork, rhea, swan, ibis, toucan.

(Puzzle 41)

101.

$$V-IV=IV$$

(Puzzle 31)

102. D. A line has been omitted from each letter in the series A, B, C, D, E, F, G, H.

(Puzzle 21)

103. 6666. Eliot could only figure out the code from the information that Drew says is sufficient if all the digits in that number are the same, otherwise he could not know in which order the digits occur. Furthermore, since he cannot determine the number from her first statement about it, the product cannot be unique and so the number cannot be 1111, 5555, 7777, 8888 or 9999. Of the remaining possibilities only 6666 meets the requirement that the first digit of the square of the product of its digits should be odd, i.e. that the square of $6 \times 6 \times 6 \times 6$ (1,296) = 1,679,616.

(Puzzle 11)

104. D. The figures in the top row are the tops of the numbers 3, 4, 5, and 7. The dots are just a disguise. The missing figure is therefore the option which corresponds with the top of the number 6.

-3-4-5-6-7--

(Puzzle 2)

105. Arrange the letters in "ten coins" to form the phrase.

(Puzzle 40)

106. 6. Two from the top side and four from the right side.

(Puzzle 30)

107. The extra cocktail stick can be arranged as shown below to produce a capital letter M on top of the existing T. When these two letters are pronounced in descending order (MT) they sound like the word empty.

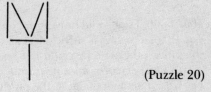

(Puzzle 20)

108. The actual time was thirty-two minutes and forty-three seconds past six at which time the hour hand was directly behind the minute hand.

(Puzzle 10)

109. Place F on the line to form E.

(Puzzle 1)

INDEX